PLANET POLICE

TREASURE SMUGGLER

Anna Nilsen • Illustrated by Real Time Visualisation

Dorling Kindersley

LONDON • NEW YORK • STUTTGART • MOSCOW

Get ready to maze race around the world!

1. Use a pencil to trace the road maze as you travel around each city.

2. You can travel along the road maze until you come to a yellow circle – this is a **flight path**.

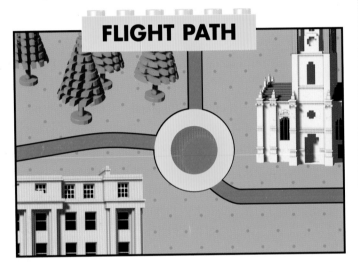

FLIGHT PATH

3. The hole in the centre of the flight path leads through to a **red landing pad** overleaf. Whenever you come across a flight path, you *must* 'fly' through to the page overleaf.

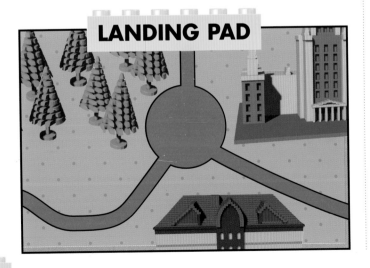

LANDING PAD

TIP: *Don't lose your position!* Before you turn the page, place the blunt end of your pencil onto the landing pad and *then* turn over.

4. On the next page you will see a new city. Trace the maze until you come to another yellow flight path. Remember – you *must* fly through!

5. If a road is blocked by a car, van, or building you must turn around and find another route.

BLOCKED ROADS

6. Make sure you go for a trial run first. See if you can get from the Police Headquarters, at the beginning of the book, to the City Jail, at the end.

POLICE HEADQUARTERS

Become a crafty criminal in *Crafty Crimes* and *Jail Break*! Or join the police force and become a police officer in *Dawn Raid*.

CRAFTY CRIMES

Be a crafty criminal! Find the route each villain took to get from their hide-out to their crime spot and back home again.

1. Use the Crafty Criminals Crime Board to find each criminal's hide-out and crime spot.

2. Decide which criminal you are going to be first, then note where their hide-out is.

3. Starting from your criminal hide-out, trace the road maze to your crime spot.

TIP: You can play each criminal in any order you like.

Planet Police Warning!
Watch out for the planet policemen! If you meet one on the road, he'll take you to the City Jail and you'll have to start again.

JAIL BREAK

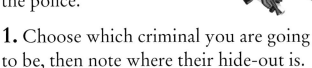

Break out of jail! Find the route each crafty criminal took to break out of jail and reach their hide-out without being caught by the police.

1. Choose which criminal you are going to be, then note where their hide-out is.

2. Starting at the City Jail, use your pencil to trace the road maze until you find your hide-out.

3. Carry on playing until you have found each criminal's route.

TIP: You can play each criminal in any order you like.

Planet Police Warning!
Watch out for the planet policemen! They'll take you back to jail and you'll have to start again!

CITY JAIL

DAWN RAID

Be a Planet Police Force Officer and make a dawn raid on those crafty criminals!

Police Force Warning!
If you come across a police motorbike on the way, this means another police officer has got to the hide-out first. You *must* go back to Police Headquarters and start again.

MISSION ONE

1. Look at the Crafty Criminals Crime Board and decide which hide-out you are going to raid first.

2. Starting from Police Headquarters, trace the road maze to the hide-out. Capture your criminal and take the villain to the City Jail, tracing the maze all the way.

MISSION TWO

Now try to capture *two* criminals in *one* trip!

1. Decide which two hide-outs you are going to raid.

2. Starting from Police Headquarters, trace the road maze to the first hide-out. Capture your criminal.

3. Continue to trace the maze until you find the second hide-out. Capture your second criminal and take *both* criminals to the City Jail.

Maze Challenge: There are **six** different ways you can catch two criminals – can you find them all?

MISSION THREE

Now try to catch *three* criminals in *one* trip!

1. Decide which three hide-outs you are going to raid.

2. Starting from Police Headquarters, trace the maze to all three hide-outs, one after the other. Capture your criminals, one-by-one, and take them to the City Jail.

Maze Challenge: There are **three** different ways to catch three criminals – can you find them?

Maze Games

MISSION FOUR
Once you've captured three criminals, you're ready for the ultimate challenge: *all four criminals in one go!*

1. Start from Police Headquarters and trace the maze to all four hide-outs, one after the other. Capture your criminals and take them to the City Jail. It's not easy, so good luck!

As you race around the world, you can see which continent you are in by matching the colour of each page border to the colour of each continent on the map below.

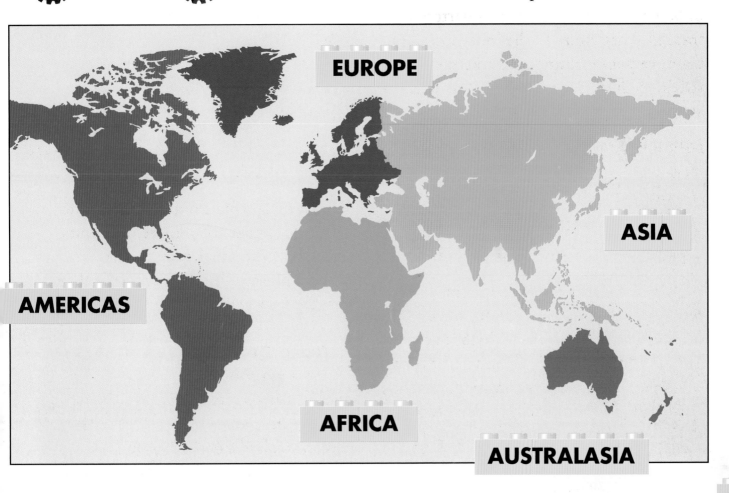

EUROPE

ASIA

AMERICAS

AFRICA

AUSTRALASIA

Planet Police
Headquarters

CRAFTY CRIMINALS CRIME BOARD

NAME
Maria Bengel

CRIME
Stole 200 boxes
of chocolate

CRIME SPOT
Sugarplum Confectioners,
Germany

HIDE-OUT
Brussels, Belgium

NAME
Rhett Ray

CRIME
Stole 50 bags of wool
from sheep farm

CRIME SPOT
Greenhills Farm,
New Zealand

HIDE-OUT
Washington, U.S.A.

NAME
Hans Mueller

CRIME
Stole truck containing
Little Mermaid statues

CRIME SPOT
The Little Mermaid statue,
Denmark

HIDE-OUT
Berlin, Germany

NAME
Isaac Fogelstein

CRIME
Stole 100 boxes
of popcorn

CRIME SPOT
Harvey's Popcorn Factory

HIDE-OUT
Jerusalem, Israel

Wave to the boats on the canal

The Tivoli amusement park

Watch out for the Planet Police!

8

March around the courtyard at Amalienborg Castle

See the famous Little Mermaid statue

COPENHAGEN
DENMARK

Congress Hall

Visit the House of World Culture, designed to look like an oyster shell

Charlottenburg Palace

Berlin University

The Reichstag stands on the line of the old Berlin Wall

BERLIN
GERMANY

Take a photo of the chariot on the Brandenburg Gate

ten to a
ncert
Karajan's
rcus

The tall
Tower of David

Hurva
Synagogue

JERUSALEM
ISRAEL

Sit by the pond at the Rockefeller Museum

Marvel at the gold on the Dome of the Rock

El Aqsa Mosque

Church of All Nations

The Centre for Performing Arts

Watch out for the Planet Police!

CHRISTCHURCH

The road is blocked – find another route!

Sail up the river but don't get stuck in the mud!

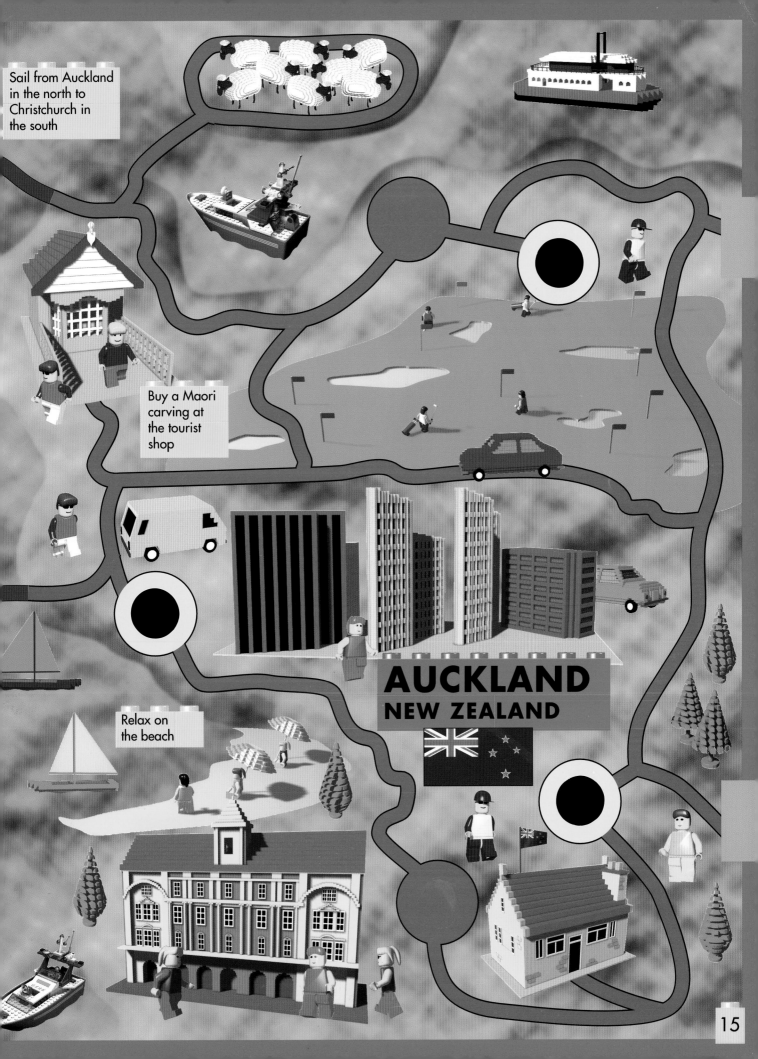

Sail from Auckland in the north to Christchurch in the south

Buy a Maori carving at the tourist shop

Relax on the beach

AUCKLAND
NEW ZEALAND

The White House

The road is blocked – find another route!

See the rockets at the National Air and Space Museum

WASHINGTON, D.C.
U.S.A.

The road is blocked – find another route!

Visit the Children's Museum at the Capitol

CHICAGO
U.S.A.

Take a ride on the giant Ferris Wheel

What is the time on the Wrigley Clock?

18

The Chicago
Theater

Chinatown

19

Climb to the highest atom of the Atomium

BRUSSELS
BELGIUM

The Grand Place

Count the pillars on the Théâtre Royal de la Monnaie

POLICE

...nt the flags by the ...Headquarters

Watch out for the Planet Police!

POLICE

See the camels at the zoo

Ride on the carousel in the park

The road is blocked – find another route!

The city market place

City Jail

BASEL
SWITZERLAND

Super Maze Games

Congratulations! You're ready for your next exciting Planet Police book and Super Dawn Raids!

Mission Preparations

1. Place both books next to each other so that the border crossings at the side of each page line up. This will let you cross from one book to another.

2. You can only cross to countries on the same continent. These countries will have the same border colour. Make sure you cross to a city which has the same border colour as the city you are leaving.

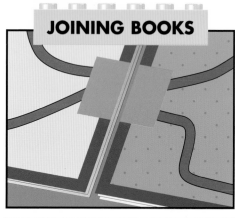

JOINING BOOKS

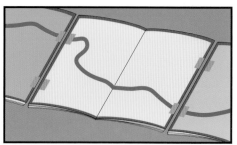

Super Mission One

1. Decide from which Police Headquarters you will start your mission and in which City Jail you'll put your criminals.

TIP: You can start from the Police Headquarters of one book and put your criminals in the City Jail of another.

2. Look at both Crafty Criminals Crime Boards and decide which crafty criminal you are going to catch first.

3. Start by capturing one criminal at a time and then build up to capturing *all eight* on just *one* trip.

Super Mission Three

1. Finally, place all four Planet Police books next to each other and then try to catch all *sixteen* crafty criminals.

Calling all Planet Police!

Remember – crafty criminals are still at large all over the world. Carry on playing to keep crime at bay!

A Dorling Kindersley Book

First published in Great Britain in 1998
by Dorling Kindersley Limited, 9 Henrietta Street, London WC2E 8PS

Text copyright © 1998 LEGO Group
Illustrations © 1998 LEGO Group
Devised and written by Anna Nilsen
Illustrated by Real Time Visualisation

Visit us on the World Wide Web at http:// www.dk.com

A CIP catalogue record for this book is available from the British Library.
ISBN 0 7513 7159 9
Colour reproduction by Flying Colours, Italy
Printed in Hong Kong

Super Mission Two

1. Now you're ready for your third Planet Police book. Place all three books next to each other, in any order you like, and set off to capture all *twelve* villains.